THE DOFLEIN METHOD

The Violinist's Progress

A course of violin instruction
combined with musical theory and practice in duet-playing
by

Erich and Elma Doflein

Text translated by Philip Marler

Progressive Pieces for three Violins

SCHOTT

Mainz · London · Berlin · Madrid · New York · Paris · Prague · Tokyo · Toronto

PREFACE

In the fifth volume of this course the study of position-playing, commenced in Volume III, is continued. The first step towards position-playing was taken in Volume III when the 2nd, 3rd and 1/2 positions were mastered. The present volume is intended to offer a detailed study of the 4th and 5th positions; the 6th and 7th positions are dealt with in basic exercises and examples, and finally a survey of the highest positions is provided.

In former violin schools playing in the higher positions was restricted usually to some *long* and *difficult* studies, which at the same time presented considerable demands on bowing technique and dexterity of the fingers. The new method of this volume is intended, on the other hand, to develop the study of higher positions with the utmost thoroughness by giving the student the opportunity of acquainting himself with the new tasks in hand step by step with the aid of numerous *short* exercises and *easy* pieces. The first examples of each new problem have been chosen in such a way that no new or difficult aspects of bowing crop up at the same time. Care has also been taken to make the use of the positions always appear obvious and sensible, so that the ear may play a decisive part in determining the position of the finger on the string.

Long passages to be played entirely in a high position occur seldom in actual music. It is however necessary for the violinist to know each position thoroughly by itself, in order to impress on his mind an exact acquaintance with the respective fingering, the span between the stops and the particular treatment of tone-production. But also for *shifting* from one position to another a certain knowledge of the position to be reached is essential, so that the way from one position to the other is not merely judged as a certain distance, but rather as leading from one familiar position on the finger-board to another just as familiar one. Only by this can certainty in free application of the various positions be attained. This purpose is served by the numerous exercises and pieces which are to be played in one of the higher positions without leaving it.

The technical exercises in *combination of the positions* are both as complete and as short as possible. In a very small compass they provide everything necessary for developing a thorough technique of position-shifting. If real success is aimed at these concentrated exercises must be practised *section by section with the utmost diligence*. The transpositions demanded of the student into other keys and on to other strings may not be omitted during this practice. The numerous pieces in which various positions are combined are not only intended to offer practice in change of position, but also to indicate to the player under which circumstances the position in question may be applied to good effect. Here, as in the whole of "The Violinist's Progress", it was our intention to combine in many examples the practice of technique, the demands of playing and the appropriate musical application of the new task.

The study and application of the fourth position are often neglected. In our course of study this position (like the second position in Volume III) is thoroughly dealt with. For it is just the sure mastery of these "intermediate positions" which paves the way to a wealth of *various*

fingerings satisfactory both from the musical and the technical point of view. The material we provide for the practice of the fifth position is just as ample. Less attention has been paid to the positions beyond the fifth, since this work is intended to provide basic knowledge and not training for virtuosity. The *scales* and *arpeggios* through several octaves have been furnished with two different fingerings in some cases: it is not enough, when performing, to have one single "standard fingering" at one's disposal.

The demands made by this volume must be fulfilled if the student wishes to attain to the technical standard required for any *fairly difficult orchestral part* and for classical and romantic *chamber music*.

Beside the easy exercises and studies there are also more difficult examples for studying all problems which arise from playing in the higher positions. Our method, and especially this volume, will be used by students of *different ages* and of very different technical and musical standards. It will therefore in some cases by necessary to restrict study at first to the easier examples, coming back to the more difficult ones at a later stage of progress.

In accordance with the material offered in this volume, less pre-classical music is included and more space is devoted to *classical music* and numerous examples from *19th century* violin schools (Campagnoli, Ries, Kayser, Alard, Bériot); it was the authors of these schools after all who were the first to pay any detailed attention to the pedagogical treatment of position-playing. In this respect our method also provides some preparation for the playing of *romantic music*.

Since the traditional technique of fingering is not adequate to certain demands of modern music, the fourth part of this volume is dedicated to this special problem. It contains in exercises and studies a selection of those problems of stopping which in modern music differ fundamentally from that of older music: whole-tone scales, chromatic passages, symmetrical sequences of identical intervals, rapid and frequent change of the attitude of the fingers within the position. In such music it is frequently necessary to depart from traditional practice and play in positions not clearly fixed; for instance, one finger may advance to a note beyond the position occupied by the hand, only to be followed subsequently by the latter, thus avoiding a slide (cf. Nos. 151, 154). Or it may be that the fingers must adopt an attitude involving several semitone steps, thus encompassing less than a fourth, in chromatic sequences (cf. Nos. 155, 156). The choice of the same fingering for identical figures in symmetrical sequences facilitates playing considerably: it however often involves regarding the notes enharmonically to achieve the right fingering. For this *free application of the positions* a certainty in the positions which were practised in the preceding chapters is absolutely necessary. On the other hand this independence in the application of the positions gained by the new technique of fingering may be regarded as an enrichment in the manner of playing older music. The exercises in this chapter in the form of extracts are also intended as practice for the ear and should therefore also be transposed.

Erich and Elma Doflein

PART I: The fourth position

A: The first finger stops the perfect fifth above the open string

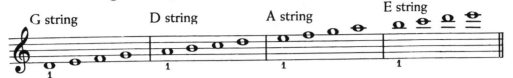

CHAPTER 1: Studies in the 4th position

1 How is the 4th position found in keys which contain the perfect fifth above the open string?

2 Four note exercises. These exercises are at first only to be practised in those keys (attitudes) in which the first finger stops the perfect fifth above the open string. The positions of the fingers for the flat keys indicated are then to be practised together with work on studies 33 to 36. The appropriate exercises should furthermore be played in attitudes corresponding to the keys of the practice-pieces as a preliminary exercise to the latter. Within the exercises the key is to be recognised by the signature; some sections however belong to several keys, such as

which can occur in D major, B minor and A major. The key required should be found on all strings.

The same exercise on the other strings (*in each case all three bars of the above four note exercises are to be played*)

4

The exercises for finding the 4th position can be altered or replaced with an eye to the key to be played; e.g.:

for E major and E minor

for A major and A minor

3 The scale of E major

4 Bohemian dance

5 The scale of A major

6 Preludio

Allegro

Michel Corrette (1738)

7 The scale of D major

8 Study *(to be practised slowly at first)*

Allegro

H. Ries (Violin School 1867)

*) The key signature in brackets is not of significance until a more advanced stage of study

9 The scale of D minor

10 Siciliano

11 Exercise in A minor

12 Harmonic study in the 4th position

Largo

E.D.

6

13 Scale exercise in E minor

14 Practice piece
Moderato

H.E. Kayser (Violin School 1867)

15 Extension of the 4th and 1st fingers

*) $\overset{\frown}{4}$ indicates that the 4th finger is to be extended upwards without change of position;
$\underset{\smile}{1}$ indicates that the first finger is drawn back a semitone without changing the position of the hand.

16 The scale of C major

17 Study
Allegretto

H.E. Kayser

CHAPTER 2: The 4th position combined with the 3rd, 2nd and 1st positions

I Combination of the 4th and 3rd positions

18 Basic exercises *The exercises are to be practised on all strings and written down*

The small intermediate notes are at first audible, played in free rhythm; they later disappear

19 Third basic exercise *(To be practised on all strings)*

20 From the Violin Concerto in A minor — A. Vivaldi

21 Andante cantabile — B. Campagnoli (Violin School 1823)

Da Capo al Fine

*) The key signatures in brackets are not of significance until a more advanced stage of study

II Combination of the 4th and 2nd positions

22 Basic exercises *(To be practised on all strings) At first only to be played in C major*

23 Change of position on a repeated note involving a change of string
Exercise

III Combination of the 4th and 1st positions

a) Change of position on one string

24 Basic exercises *All basic exercises are to be practised on each string*

25 Third basic exercise

b) Direct entry into the 4th position

26 Basic exercise *(To be practised on all strings)*

27 Exercise

28 Themes by J.S. Bach

1) From the Violin Concerto in E major; end of the 1st movement

2) From the Partita in E major for Violin alone, Prelude

*) The key signature in brackets is not of significance until a more advanced stage of study

c) Change of position combined with change of string

29 Exercise in the form of a slow waltz

30 The higher position on the lower string[x)] *a)* E major; *b)* E minor

*) The repetitions are an important element of the exercises and may not be passed over

31 Allegro

C. Ph. E. Bach (1770)

32 Scales and triads
E major and E minor

To be played with different kinds of bowing

B: The first finger stops the diminished fifth above the open string

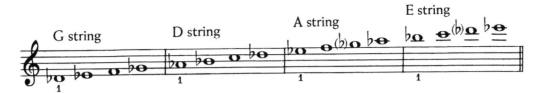

CHAPTER 3: Studies in the 4th position

33 How is the 4th position to be found in keys containing the diminished fifth above the open string?

The four note exercises of No.2 on page 3 are now to be practised in the various attitudes with 1st finger lower on the string: On the E and A strings attitudes d) e) f), on the D and G strings attitudes e) f)

The scale of E flat major is now to be played in the 4th position; form and fingering as in scale exercise No.3 (E major)

34 Song   J.A.P. Schultz (1747—1800)

Sun - shine foll-ows the show - ers, Hosts of glo - ri - ous flow - ers Burst in-to bloom o'er the lea.

Scen - ted bree-zes are play - ing New-born bird-lets are sway - ing In their nests in the sha - dy tree.

The scale of A flat major is now to be practised in the 4th position (see No.5)

35 Study in triads   Hubert Ries (Violin School 1867)

No.7 is to be practised with the key signature of D flat major

36 Prelude   after Michel Corrette (1738)

CHAPTER 4: The fourth position combined with the lower positions

I Combination of the 4th and 3rd positions

The exercises of No. 18 are now to be practised in the flat keys. Final notes according to the keys played

Exercise No. 19 is now to be practised in A flat major

37 Change of position involving change of string

38 Allegro scherzando

C. Ph. E. Bach (1770)

II Combination of the 4th and 2nd positions

The exercises of No. 22 are now to be played in C minor

39 Duet

J. Aubert (1730)

40 **Study** Allegro agitato

H. Ries

III Combination of the 4th and 1st positions

The exercises No.24, I and II are now to be played in E flat major and A flat major (corresponding keys on the other strings)

41 **Second basic exercise** *To be practised on all strings*

Exercise No.25 is now to be played in E flat major

42 **Theme from the "Symphonie concertante"**

W. A. Mozart (1779)

Presto

43 From a Sonata for violin and piano (op. 12 No. 3)

L. van Beethoven (1799)

Allegro molto

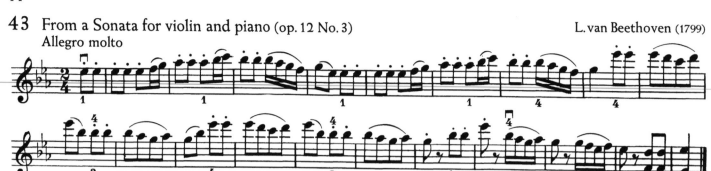

The scale and triads of E flat major through two octaves are now to be practised with fingering as in No. 32

Exercise No. 27 is now to be played in G minor

CHAPTER 5: Application of the 4th position

44 Andante

B. Campagnoli

45 Andante

C.Ph.E. Bach (Hamburg 1770)

46 Andante *)

Carlo Tessarini (Violin School 1734)

47 Tambourin

Presto

G. Guillemain (1705—1770)

Da Capo al Fine

*) This piece is intended by Tessarini as a study for playing in the 4th position. If however the player remains in this position it is entirely satisfactory neither from the point of view of technique nor of tone quality. Thus fingering has been chosen here more adapted to the beauty of the melody.

48 Ten variations in classical style on a folk song (application of all changes of position)

Andante grazioso

Variation 1

Var. 2

Var. 3

Var. 4

Var. 5 Minore

Var. 10

49 Caprice

Franz Benda (1709—1786)

50 Tempo di Menuetto

Hubert Ries

PART II: The fifth position

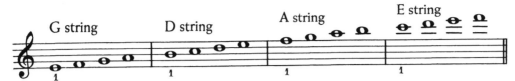

CHAPTER 6: Studies in the 5th position

A: The first finger stops the minor sixth above the open string

First the keys and attitudes of the fingers should be studied in which the 1st finger stops the minor sixth above the open string: Exercises 51 and 52 are therefore here only to be played in the flat keys

51 How is the fifth position to be found?   The key signatures in brackets are not of significance until a more advanced stage of study

52 Four note exercises

The same exercises on the other strings *(In each case all three bars are to be played)*

53 **Allegretto** *(Also to be played a fifth higher)*   H.E. Kayser (Violin School 1867)

54 Quickly *(Also to be played a fifth higher)*

55 Scale study *(E flat major and B flat major)* *To be played without slurs at first*

56 F major

B: The first finger stops the major sixth above the open string

Exercises 51 and 52 are now to be played in the keys and attitudes of the fingers in which the first finger stops the major sixth above the open string: No. 53 is here to be played a semitone higher in E major *(Beware, Violin II: half position!)*

57 Andante *(Also to be played a fifth higher)*

H.E. Kayser

58 Allegro moderato

H.E. Kayser

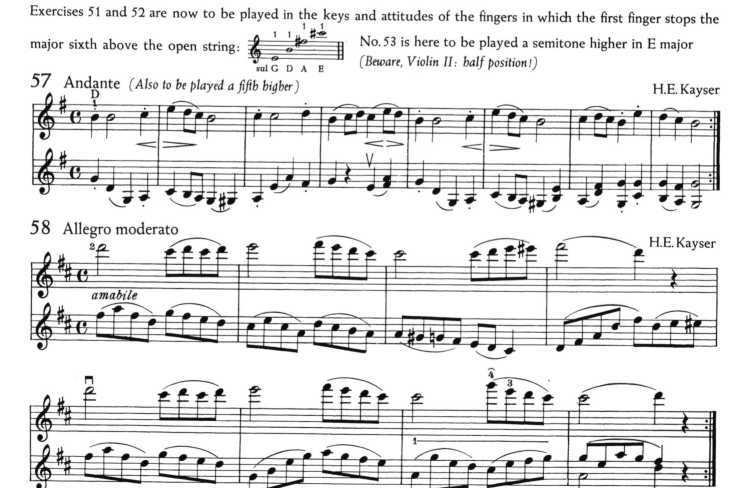

59 Rumanian shepherd's melody

60 Study over all four strings *(The lower part is to be played by the teacher as a help to pure intonation)*

C: The first finger stands in turn a minor or a major sixth above the open string

The exercise of No. 52 are now to be played going through all attitudes of the fingers

61 Study

after Bériot (Violin School)

62 Practice Piece

Andante

63 Larghetto

D. Alard (Violin School 1848)

64 Extensions within the 5th position *To be practised on all strings*

a) A semitone

b) A whole tone

65 Study for the G string

Broadly

66 Larghetto *)

B. Campagnoli

*) From one of the Divertimenti for Studying the Seven Positions, op. 18

CHAPTER 7: The fifth position combined with the lower positions

I Combination of the 5th and 3rd positions

a) Change of position without change of string

67 Basic exercise *(To be practised on all strings)*

68 Exercises for all manners of combining the 1st, 3rd and 5th positions

69 Serenade

Allegretto grazioso

G. B. Viotti (1753—1824)

70 Viennese waltz for two violins

J. Mayseder (1789—1863)

Fine

D. C. al Fine

b) Change of position involving change of string

71 Exercise

1.)

2.)

72 The Cuckoo

73 The higher position on the lower string

*) The repetitions are an important element of the exercises and may not be passed over

II Combination of the 5ᵗʰ and 4ᵗʰ positions
(Also involving the 3ʳᵈ position)

74 Combination of the 4ᵗʰ and 5ᵗʰ positions

Also to be practised in E and E flat major

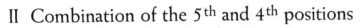

75 Adagio
after Fr. Geminiani

76 Study

A. Rolla (1798—1837)

Moderato

77 Study in high chromatic notes

Slowly

E.D.

III Combination of the 5th and 1st positions

a) Change of position without change of string

78 Basic exercises *To be practised on all strings and in different keys*

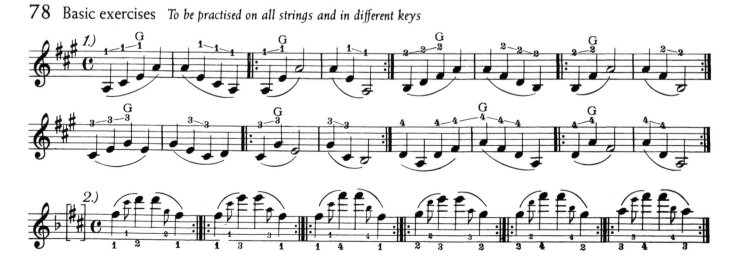

79 Third basic exercise   Scales and triads on one string
(To be practised on all strings)

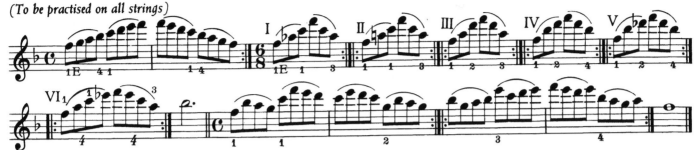

With the exception of triads I and V these exercises are all to be practised with the key signature of D major also

80 Allegro moderato

from a duet by J.F.Mazas

81 Poco Adagio

Andreas Romberg (1767—1821)

*) Trill commences with the upper note, C sharp

b) Direct entry into the 5th position

82 Exercise

83 Viennese waltz for two violins   J. Mayseder

Fine

D. C. al Fine

c) Change of position combined with change of string

84 The echo *(The higher position on the lower string)*

85 Study

Adagio

H.E. Kayser

86 The scales of G major and G minor and triads
through three octaves

Also to be played slurred

IV Combination of the 5th and 2nd positions

87 Three exercises *(Also to be practised on the other strings)*

88 Rondo-theme from the Spring Sonata

Allegro moderato

L. van Beethoven, op. 24 (1801)

Variation of this theme

89 F major and F minor over two octaves

Also to be played slurred

F sharp major and F sharp minor can be played with the same fingering

V Two studies with application of the 5th position

90 Caprice

Andantino

A. Rolla (1798—1837)

91 Study

Allegro moderato

H. E. Kayser

VI All hitherto practised positions are approached from the 1st and 5th positions

92 Exercises

VII Five slow movements with application of the 5th position

93 Adagio

Fr. Geminiani

94 Andante affettuoso

A. Romberg

95 Andante

P. Rode (1774—1830)

96 Adagio

B. Campagnoli (Violin School)

97 Serenade on the G string

after D. Alard

Allegretto

PART III: Sixth to tenth positions
CHAPTER 8: The sixth position and its application
I Studies in the sixth position

98 How is the 6th position to be found?

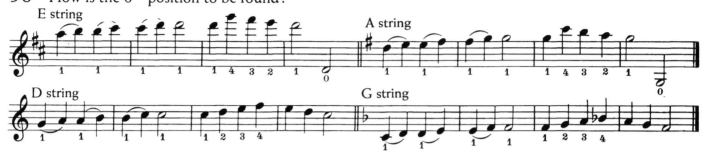

Note: the same fingering applies for the 6th position as for the 2nd position; in other words the notes which are stopped in the **2nd position** on the E string are to be found in the 6th position on the A string. In like manner: 2nd position A string = 6th position D string; 2nd position D string = 6th position G string. (The high notes of the 6th position on the E string are of course an exception). There is a similar correspondence between the 7th and 3rd positions.

99 Four note exercise in the 6th position

100 G major in the 6th position *Also to be played with the keysignature of G minor (harmonic)*

101 Exercise for large intervals in the 6th position

102 Practice piece
Poco Adagio

H.E.Kayser

II Combining the 6th position with the lower positions

a) From the 5th to the 6th position

103 Basic exercise *To be practised in various keys*

104 Further exercises

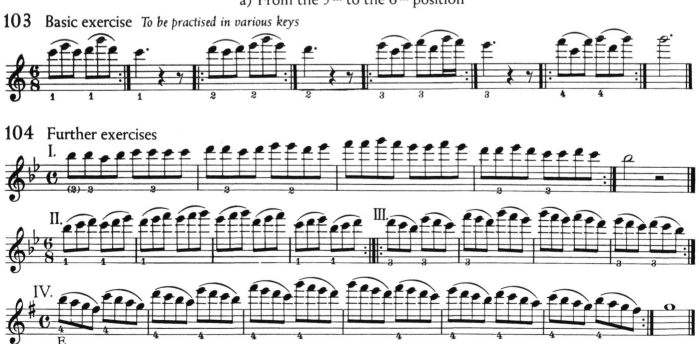

J.S.Bach

105 From the Chaconne for Violin alone

b) From the 4th to the 6th position

106 From a String Trio (op. 3 No. 1)

L. van Beethoven

Moderato

107 Exercise

108 Extension of the 4th finger

from a Study by P. Rode

c) From the 3rd to the 6th position

109 Exercises

1.)

2.) The exercises of No. 87 (page 34, 2nd to the 5th position) are now to be transposed a note higher, to be written down in the new key and to be practised with shifts from the 3rd to the 6th position

3.)

110 Allegro (Trio from the Scherzo of String Quartet No. 38)
The fingering is the composer's; it is to stress the amusing character of the piece

Joseph Haydn (1781)

*) The second part has been adapted

111 Molto Allegro

from a String Quartet by W. A. Mozart

d) Playing on the G string

112 Hungarian folk-song

from: B. Bartók's Collection of folk-songs *)

espressivo

*) From "Das ungarische Volkslied" by B. Bartók, Ungarische Bibliothek Vol. XI (publ. W. de Gruyter, Berlin)

113 Adagio on the G string

B. Campagnoli

e) From the 1st to the 6th position

114 Three exercises

f) Scales and triads over three octaves up to the 6th position

115 G major and G minor

also to be played slurred

G sharp minor

A major and A minor

A flat major is to be played with the same fingering

CHAPTER 9: The seventh position

I Studies in the 7th position

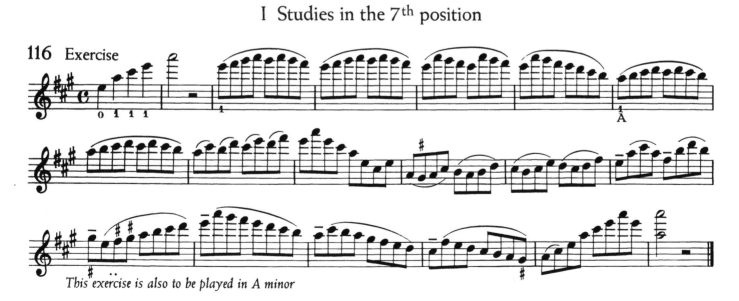

116 Exercise

This exercise is also to be played in A minor

117 Andantino quasi Allegretto

H.E.Kayser

118 Poco vivace

H.E.Kayser

II Combining the 7th position with the lower positions

a) From the 6th to the 7th position

119 Exercise

The exercises of No.104 are now each to be extended one figure into the 7th position. Furthermore they can be transposed a note higher: I, II and III into C major, 4th to 7th position; IV to A major, 2nd to 7th position. The transposed notes should be written down.

120 From the 1st movement of the Violin Concerto in C major   Joseph Haydn

b) From the 5th to the 7th position

121 Exercise

122 Theme from the final movement of Quartet No.29 (adapted)   Joseph Haydn

48

123 Allegro assai

From a duet by F.W. Rust (1739—1796)

124 Scale exercises *(To be practised on all strings)*

1.) sul G

2.) sul D

3.) sul A

125 First theme of the 1ˢᵗ movement of the Violin Concerto in D major

Allegro

W.A. Mozart

c) From the 3rd and 4th to the 7th position

126 Four exercises *(To be practised on all strings)*

127 Theme from the 3rd movement of the "Symphonie concertante"

W. A. Mozart

d) From the 1st to the 7th position

128

The exercise is to be practised on all strings

129 Scales and triads up to the 7th position

a) A major and A minor

Also to be played slurred

A flat *be played with the same fingering*

b) B flat major and B flat minor

B major and B minor are to be played with the same fingering

e) Application of the 7th position
(Playing on one string)

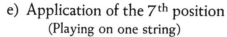

130 Larghetto

B. Campagnoli (Violin School)

à mono corde
(= on one string)

131 Study for the G string

Adagio

Federigo Fiorillo (1753—1823)

132 From a duet for violin and viola

Joseph Haydn

133 From a study

P. Rode

134 Fantasia for violin alone
Allegro

Michel Corrette
(Violin School 1738)

simile (arpeggio to be continued)

arpeggio continued

*) The composer's fingering

CHAPTER 10:

Exercises and examples in application of the 8th, 9th and 10th positions

a) Up to the 8th position

Some of the exercises in position-shifting up to the 7th position (Chapter 9) can now be transposed a note higher so that they extend to the 8th position: No. 119 is to be played in D major, starting in the 6th position; No. 128 is to be played in G major and G minor on the E string, starting in the 2nd position with the 1st finger. The transposed notes are to be written down in any case.

135 Shifting from the 4th to the 6th to the 8th position

136 Allegretto (Trio of the minuet from String Quartet No. 57)

Jos. Haydn

*dolce
*)

*) The second part has been adapted

137 Study

Allegro giusto

Antonio Rolla

138 From the "Symphonie concertante" for violin and viola

W.A. Mozart

Allegro maestoso

139 Theme

Paul Hindemith
String Trio (1924)

140 Study (shortened)

F. Fiorillo

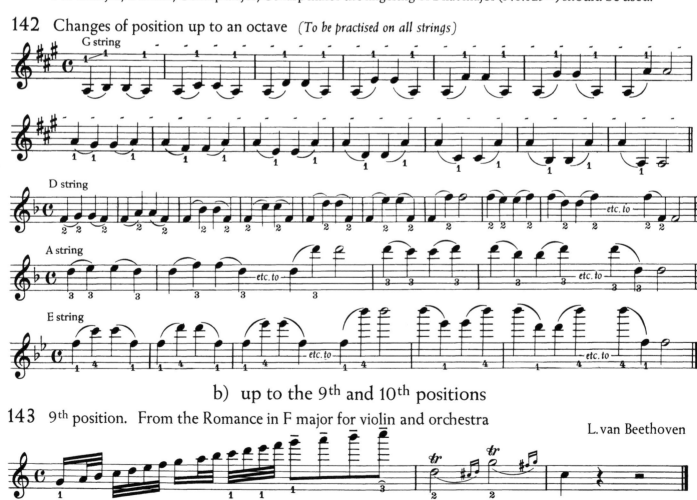

Here may be mentioned the well-known study by Kreutzer (No. 12), which contains triads over three octaves up to the 8th position.

141 Scales and triads over three octaves up to the 8th position

B flat major, B flat minor, B major, B minor; these should be played starting in the 2nd position with the corresponding fingering with which A major was played from the 1st to the 7th position in No. 129. For C major, C minor, C sharp major, C sharp minor the fingering of B flat major (No. 129 b)) should be used.

142 Changes of position up to an octave *(To be practised on all strings)*

b) **up to the 9th and 10th positions**

143 9th position. From the Romance in F major for violin and orchestra

L. van Beethoven

144 From the String Quartet op. 54 II   J. Haydn

145 From the 1st movement of the Violin Concerto in A major   W. A. Mozart

Allegro aperto

146 10th position. From the "Symphonie concertante" (3rd movement)   W. A. Mozart

147 From the String Quartet op 54 II   J. Haydn

148 From a study   R. Kreutzer

149 Scales and triads over three octaves up to the 9th and 10th positions

The 9th position is reached in: C major, C minor, C sharp major, C sharp minor; these should be played, starting in the 3rd position, with the corresponding fingering with which A major was played in No. 129. For D flat major, D major, D minor the fingering of B flat major (No. 129 b) should be used. The 10th position is reached in: D flat major, D major, D minor; with extension of the 4th finger also E flat major, E flat minor, E major, E minor. The fingering, starting in the 4th or 5th position, corresponds to that of No. 129 b) B flat major.

150 Study

Adagio espressivo

F. Fiorillo

PART IV: Techniques of stopping in modern music
The whole-tone scale, chromatic passages, symmetric intervals

I The whole-tone scale and its application

151 The whole-tone scale *(Also to be commenced on other notes)*

152 The augmented fourth *)

153 Major thirds in intervals of whole-tones *)

154 Whole-tone figures in chromatic sequence *)

*) Exercises on one string should also be transposed for the other strings. Writing down is recommended, especially for the E string

II Chromatic passages

155

1. The chromatic scale   *a) over several strings*

b) on one string

2. Groups of six notes   *a) sextuplets*

b) triplets

156 Pairs of whole-tones ascending and descending chromatically

III Repetition of similar figures, symmetric intervals

157 Fourths

to be continued ad lib.

158 Study of the major third

Allegro

Harald Genzmer (1949)

mf

159 Minor thirds

1.Diminished fourths between 1st and 4th finger

a)

b) The inversion

2.

3.

H.Genzmer (1949)

160 Study of the minor third

Allegro

161 Study

Presto

E.D.

162 Minor sixths *)

*) Preliminary exercise

Kinds of bowing

163 Study

Harald Genzmer (1949)

IV Rapid change of attitude within the position

164 Study

Vivace

Walter Heck (1949)

165 Study
Vivace

Walter Heck (1949)

166 .... The weather is so fine outside

In easy motion

Paul Hindemith
1st movement of the Sonata for Violin alone, op. 31 Nr. 2